G000296831

Nelson

GRAMMAR

COPYMASTERS

FOR BOOKS 1 AND 2

WENDY WREN

Contents

Nelson

Design: Clive Sutherland
Editorial: Liz Harman
Illustration: Jenny Tulip

© Wendy Wren 1998

First published by Thomas Nelson & Sons Ltd 1998

Reprinted in 2001 by:
Nelson Thornes Ltd
Delta Place
27 Bath Road
CHELTENHAM
GL53 7TH
United Kingdom

ISBN 0-17-424720-6

03 04 05 / 10 9 8 7 6 5

Printed in Croatia by Zrinski

Nelson

GRAMMAR

Individual Record Sheet

Name: --

Copymaster	✓	Comment
Pupil Book 1		
Unit 1 Nouns		
Unit 2 Adjectives		
Unit 3 Singular and plural		
Unit 4 Prepositions		
Unit 5 Proper nouns		
Unit 6 Pronouns		
Unit 7 Confusing words		
Unit 8 Nouns		
Unit 9 Adjectives		
Unit 10 Sentences		
Unit 11 Verbs		
Unit 12 Questions		
Unit 13 Verbs		
Unit 14 Adjectives		
Unit 15 Conjunctions		
Unit 16 Verbs		
Unit 17 Pronouns		
Unit 18 Adjectives		
Unit 19 Conjunctions		
Pupil Book 2		
Unit 1 Proper nouns		
Unit 2 Adjectives		
Unit 3 Confusing words		
Unit 4 Conjunctions		
Unit 5 Verbs		
Unit 6 Verbs		
Unit 7 Proper nouns		
Unit 8 Verbs		
Unit 9 Adjectives		
Unit 10 Contractions		
Unit 11 Adverbs		
Unit 12 Prepositions		
Unit 13 Articles		
Unit 14 Verbs		
Unit 15 Confusing words		
Unit 16 Singular and plural		
Unit 17 Adverbs		
Unit 18 Verbs		
Unit 19 Sentences		
Improve Your Writing copymasters		
1 Using adjectives		
2 Using prepositions		
3 Using proper nouns and pronouns		
4 Using interesting verbs		
5 Using conjunctions		
6 Using adverbs		
7 Using adjectives and adverbs		

name _____ date _____

A Underline the **nouns**.

cage	run	grass	house	happy
red	lamp	desk	telephone	over
fence	in	box	he	chair

B Write six **nouns** you can find in a supermarket.

------------------------ ------------------------ ------------------------

------------------------ ------------------------ ------------------------

C Write six **nouns** you can find in the garden.

------------------------ ------------------------ ------------------------

------------------------ ------------------------ ------------------------

D Use **nouns** to fill the gaps.

The bird pecked at the _____.
It was looking for _____. It
found a _____ and caught it
in its _____. The bird flew to
the top of a _____ to eat its
_____.

Nelson Grammar © Wendy Wren 1998 Published by Thomas Nelson and Sons Ltd.

name _____ date _____

A Underline the **adjectives**.

happy	find	wicked	miserable	cupboard	she
beautiful	jar	house	old	cold	telephone

B Write four **adjectives** to describe each picture.

----------------- -----------------   ----------------- -----------------

----------------- -----------------   ----------------- -----------------

C Describe what you look like.
Use as many **adjectives** as you can.

Nelson Grammar © Wendy Wren 1998   Published by Thomas Nelson and Sons Ltd.

A Write the correct **plural** words in the gaps.
The pictures will help you.

1 I took my _____ to the park.

2 If you drop the _____ they will break.

3 The _____ made a nest in the tree.

4 The _____ are painted red.

5 Please fetch some _____ .

B Underline the **plural** words.

cars	book	tiger	elephants	buns
cup	trees	ball	desks	windows

C Write the **singular** words for these plurals.

	singular	plural
1	_____	walls
2	_____	peas
3	_____	plants
4	_____	tractors

A Underline the **prepositions**.

bottle	over	hand	inside	jumps	laughing	in
	down	pencil	it	on	under	cap
outside	knock	up	light	off	out	sign

B Write a **preposition** in each gap to complete the sentences.

1 The dog buried his bone _____ a bush.

2 It is very windy _____ .

3 Look _____ the cupboard for your shoes.

4 I go _____ the stairs in the morning.

5 Get _____ the bus when you reach the shops.

C Write a sentence about each picture.
Each sentence must have a **preposition**.

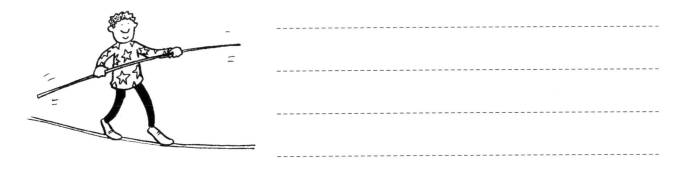

_____

_____

_____

_____

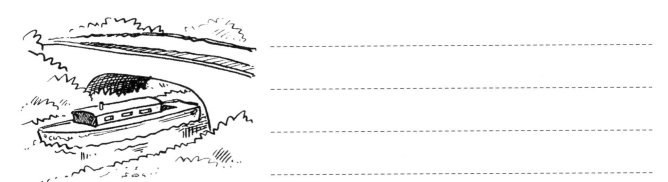

_____

_____

_____

A Write these **proper nouns**, putting in the capital letters.

1 paul smith ....
2 aftab raja ....
3 carlton barret ....
4 maria garcia ....

5 victor grant ....
6 sarah brown ....
7 daisy harris ....
8 tom finch ....

B Write the **name** of a person that starts with each of these letters.

J ....
S ....
W ....
D ....

R ....
B ....
L ....
N ....

P ....
C ....
M ....
T ....

C Choose **names** for the boy, his cat, his dog and his bird.

The boy is called ....
The cat is called ....
The dog is called ....
The bird is called ....

A Underline the **pronouns**.

she	boy	it	woman
they	elephant	he	girl

B Fill each gap with a **pronoun**.

1 _____ is sleeping.

2 _____ is cycling.

3 _____ is washing.

4 _____ are painting.

C Copy the sentences below.
Replace the underlined words with **pronouns**.

1 <u>Ryan and Sam</u> were late for school.

----

2 <u>The woman</u> walked quickly down the street.

----

3 <u>The birds</u> flew south for the winter.

A Add *two* or *to* to these signs.

1

.... shopping days before Christmas

2
.... the zoo

3
Tickets .... pounds

4
Next ferry at .... o' clock

5
..............- way traffic

B Fill each gap with *two* or *to*.

1 I am going .... write a letter.

2 Please buy .... pounds of apples.

3 In .... minutes the bell will ring.

4 Can we go .... the swimming pool?

5 This path leads .... the village.

C Write a sentence using the word *two*.

D Write a sentence using the word *to*.

Nelson Grammar © Wendy Wren 1998 Published by Thomas Nelson and Sons Ltd.

A Underline the **common nouns**.
Put rings around the **proper nouns**.

cart	Sam	Sanjay	flower	jump
Mr Brown	horse	Tina	sad	carpet
Tracy	frog	tent	singing	Miss Swift	wet

B Write a sentence for each picture.
Use at least one **noun** and one **proper noun** in each.
Underline the nouns and the proper nouns.

1

_____

_____

2

_____

_____

3

_____

_____

4

_____

_____

C Write your own name.

_____

Nelson

BOOK 1
Unit 9
Copymaster

GRAMMAR

name _____   date _____

Look at this picture.

Nelson Grammar © Wendy Wren 1998 Published by Thomas Nelson and Sons Ltd.

Use the picture and the **adjectives** in the box to write some sentences about the panda and what it is eating.

large	black	white	tall	thin
fat	long	green	furry	

Nelson
BOOK 1
Unit 10
Copymaster

GRAMMAR

name _____

date _____

A Write the correct **sentence** under each picture.

> The astronaut climbed out of the spaceship.
>
> The door of the spaceship opened.
>
> The astronaut was frightened by the alien.
>
> The spaceship landed on the planet.

A Underline the **verbs**.

hopping	cold	making	hat	likes
window	shout	sleeping	falls	shoe
goes	green	basket	bookcase	sing

B Write three **verbs** to show what each of these can do.

1

2

\-   \-

\-   \-

\-   \-

C Read the sentences below.
Underline the **verbs**.

1   The ship sails on the sea.

2   I read my book until bedtime.

3   The wind blows out the candle.

4   The clock ticks loudly.

5   Many people like fish and chips.

Nelson Grammar © Wendy Wren 1998   Published by Thomas Nelson and Sons Ltd.

A Imagine that a new boy or girl has joined your class.
Write three **questions** that you would like to ask the new pupil.

1 --

----

2 --

----

3 --

B These are question words:

who   what   where   when   why

Write a **question** starting with each question word.

1 --

----

2 --

----

3 --

----

4 --

----

5 --

A Underline the best **verb** for each picture.

1

feeds   sleeps   jumps

2

breaks   bends   shakes

3

climbs   runs   walks

4

sits   holds   rides

B Use each of these **verbs** in a sentence of your own.

1 laughs _____

_____

2 buys _____

_____

3 creeps _____

_____

4 shouts _____

_____

Nelson Grammar © Wendy Wren 1998 Published by Thomas Nelson and Sons Ltd.

Colour this picture.

Write some sentences to describe the clown.
Use **colour adjectives** in your sentences.

A Underline the **two short sentences** that have been joined to make each of these longer sentences.

1 Last night it was very windy and the fence blew down.

2 We had pasta for lunch and I ate it all.

3 On hot days we go to the seaside and we swim in the sea.

4 The dog barked at the postwoman and she dropped the letters.

5 I fell over and I hurt my knee.

B Use *and* to join these pairs of sentences.

1 It rained all day.
  I got wet going to school.

_____

_____

2 The football went over the wall.
  We couldn't find it.

_____

_____

3 Two boys in class are very tall.
  They both have brown hair.

_____

_____

Nelson Grammar © Wendy Wren 1998 Published by Thomas Nelson and Sons Ltd.

A Underline the **verb family names** in these sentences.

1 I like to go to the zoo.

2 To write neatly you must take your time.

3 If you want to read you must go somewhere quiet.

4 I would like to live in Australia.

5 I need to find my ticket.

B Write three verbs belonging to each **verb family name**.

1 to roll	2 to pick	3 to wander
---------------------	---------------------	---------------------
---------------------	---------------------	---------------------
---------------------	---------------------	---------------------

C Write the **verb family names** of these verbs.

1	come	comes	coming	---
2	find	finds	finding	--
3	dig	digs	digging	--
4	skip	skips	skipping	---
5	hope	hopes	hoping	---

name _____   date _____

A Underline the **pronouns** in each sentence.

1 When Aziz eats jelly he makes a mess.

2 I can never find my key when I need it.

3 We must mend the broken window.

4 They come to collect the rubbish on Wednesday.

5 The floor is dirty and it needs washing.

B Rewrite these sentences, using **pronouns** to make them sound better.

1 When my brother and I get our pocket money my brother and I go to the shops.

----

2 Sara has a bicycle and Sara cycles to school.

----

3 Simon likes chocolate and Simon eats it every day.

----

4 When the girls play netball the girls like to win.

Nelson Grammar © Wendy Wren 1998 Published by Thomas Nelson and Sons Ltd.

A Write the **number adjectives**.

1 = _one_____   2 = _____

3 = _____   4 = _____

5 = _____   6 = _____

7 = _____   8 = _____

9 = _____   10 = _____

B Underline the **number adjectives** in these sentences.

1   There are sixteen apples on the tree.

2   This plate is two hundred years old.

3   There are eleven players in a football team.

4   We have five cats, two dogs and one hamster.

5   Twenty-five people got on the bus.

C Put each of these **number adjectives** into a sentence.

1 _fifty-two_ _____

_____

2 _seventeen_ _____

_____

A Underline the **two short sentences** that have been joined to
make each of these longer sentences.

1   I hate eating sprouts but I have to have them every Sunday.

2   Shobu wanted to go out but it was too wet.

3   The runner hurt his foot but he won the race.

4   You can have an ice-cream now but you can't have one tomorrow.

5   The rain poured down but the old roof didn't leak.

B Use *and* or *but* to join each pair of sentences.

1   Please find a pencil.
    Bring it to me.

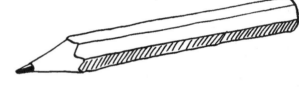

----

2   Take that glass to the kitchen.
    Don't take the other one.

----

3   My bicycle got stuck in the mud.
    I managed to get it out.

Nelson Grammar © Wendy Wren 1998 Published by Thomas Nelson and Sons Ltd.

Nelson

BOOK 2

Unit 1

Copymaster

GRAMMAR

name _____   date _____

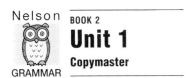

Look at this map.
It has: three villages
         a river
         hills
         a wood
         a lake.
There are no names on the map.
Make up your own names and write them on the map.

A Look at the sentences below.
Underline all the **adjectives**.
Put a ring around the **comparative adjectives**.

1   The people waited on the crowded platform.

2   The train was late.

3   "It was later than this yesterday," said one man.

4   "We need a faster train," said another.

5   "It doesn't matter," said one passenger. "Even if the train is late, it is quicker than walking!"

B Complete this table.

Adjective	Comparative adjective
soft	_____
strong	_____
large	_____
great	_____
sharp	_____
old	_____
bright	_____

C Write two sentences using **comparative adjectives**.

1   _____

    _____

2   _____

    _____

Nelson Grammar © Wendy Wren 1998 Published by Thomas Nelson and Sons Ltd.

Nelson
GRAMMAR

BOOK 2
Unit 3
Copymaster

name _____ date _____

A Write *two*, *to* or *too* in each gap.

1 _____ and _____ make four.

2 There are _____ many flowers in this vase.

3 Go _____ bed and read your book.

4 You must find out where we have _____ go.

5 I would like some cake _____ .

6 If you eat _____ many sweets you will have _____
   go _____ the dentist.

7 I am taking _____ pounds _____ the shops
   _____ buy some fruit.

8 You can pack _____ pairs of shoes but make sure your
   case is not _____ heavy.

B Write a sentence using each pair of words below.
Use them in the order that they are written.

1 to too _____

   _____

2 two to _____

   _____

A Change the underlined words into **pronouns**.
Join each pair of sentences using *and, but, so* or *because*.

1 Ella wanted her tea early. <u>Ella</u> was hungry.

----

2 Kerry wanted to put her boots on. <u>Kerry</u> could not find them.

----

3 The snake slithered along the ground. <u>The snake</u> hid under a rock.

B Write a sentence that uses each of these **conjunctions**.

and 1 ---

----

but 2 ---

----

so 3 ---

----

because 4 ---

Nelson Grammar © Wendy Wren 1998 Published by Thomas Nelson and Sons Ltd.

name _____ date _____

Use the **present tense** to write about what is happening in the picture.
Underline all the **present tense verbs** you use.

Nelson
GRAMMAR
BOOK 2
Unit 6
Copymaster

name _____   date _____

A Choose an ending from the box for each sentence below.
Work out all your sentences before you start writing.

> are very muddy.
> is very cold today.
> is asleep.
> am in the garden.
> are lost.

1 He _____

2 I _____

3 They _____

4 We _____

5 It _____

B Fill each gap with *am, is* or *are*.

1 I _____ going to join the school choir.

2 The dog _____ black and white.

3 You and I _____ best friends.

4 The postwoman and the milkman _____ up early
every morning.

5 Sophie said, "I _____ the smallest girl in the class."

6 Louise _____ captain of the hockey team.

name _____   date _____

A Can you sort out these jumbled letters?
They make the names of the days of the week.

auaStrdy   ueaydsT   rFdiya

------------------   ------------------   ------------------

dyaMno   rdhuTsay   eensaWddy

------------------   ------------------   ------------------

dynSau

B Fill the gaps with the names of the missing months.

January   _____   March   _____

May   _____   July   _____

September   _____   November   _____

A Copy the sentences below.
Change the underlined word into the **present tense**.
Use the verb 'to be' and 'ing'.
The first one has been done for you.

1 The traffic <u>speeds</u> along the motorway.

   The traffic <u>is speeding</u> along the motorway.

2 If you <u>go</u> to the library, will you take back my book?

   ----

3 They <u>pack</u> sandwiches for a picnic lunch.

   ----

4 We <u>take</u> boots with us in case it rains.

   ----

5 I <u>do</u> my homework before I go out.

B Change these verbs to the **present tense** by adding *ing*.
Watch your spelling!

1 smile _____ 2 shine _____ 3 bake _____

4 drive _____ 5 write _____ 6 make _____

C Choose five of the 'ing' words from part B and use each one in a sentence.

1 --

2 --

3 --

4 --

5 --

Aisha

Tom

Hasan

A Use **adjectives** from the box to fill the gaps in the sentences below.

taller	smallest	tallest
smaller	small	tall

1 Aisha is _____ .

2 Hasan is _____ .

3 Tom is _____ than Aisha and _____ than Hasan.

4 Hasan is _____ than Tom and Aisha.

5 Aisha is the _____ of the three children.

6 Hasan is the _____ of the three children.

B Use these **superlative adjectives** in sentences of your own.

1 highest _____

_____

2 saddest _____

_____

3 deepest _____

_____

Nelson
GRAMMAR
BOOK 2
Unit 10
Copymaster

name _____ date _____

A In each of the sentences below, there are pairs of words that can be made into **contractions**.
Underline each pair and write the contraction they make.
The first one has been done for you.

1 <u>She is</u> looking for her sister. .....She's.....

2 On Saturday I am going to a birthday party. ....

3 We are going to move to a new house next year. ....

4 I know he is leaving at lunch time. ....

5 They are going to see their uncle. ....

6 You should be happy that you are in the team. ....

7 On cold days it is sensible to wear a coat. ....

B Write the words that made the **contractions** below.
The apostrophe shows where a letter or letters have been missed out.

1 doesn't .... 2 isn't ....

3 I've .... 4 hadn't ....

5 I'll .... 6 wouldn't ....

7 aren't .... 8 who's ....

9 can't .... 10 they've ....

Nelson Grammar © Wendy Wren 1998 Published by Thomas Nelson and Sons Ltd.

A Underline the **adverbs** in these sentences.

1 Please move quickly to your next lesson.

2 You can tidy your books later.

3 I often go swimming.

4 Put the pencils here and the paper there.

5 I never eat prawns.

6 She wrote slowly and carefully.

B Look at the **adverbs** in the box. Write each one in the correct place on the table.

How?	When?	Where?
------------	------------	------------
------------	------------	------------
------------	------------	------------
------------	------------	------------
------------	------------	------------
------------	------------	------------

soon   happily
far   badly   then
swiftly   near
everywhere   now
early   angrily

C Put a **how adverb**, a **when adverb** and a **where adverb** in sentences of your own.

1 how? --

----

2 when? --

----

3 where? --

Nelson Grammar © Wendy Wren 1998   Published by Thomas Nelson and Sons Ltd.

Nelson BOOK 2

Unit 12

Copymaster

GRAMMAR

name _____

date _____

A Can you find the six **prepositions** hidden in the wordsearch?
Put rings around them.

x	g	i	n	t	o	o	f	g
b	h	i	x	a	p	t	n	u
b	w	r	u	n	e	a	r	x
e	b	u	o	n	a	z	o	p
h	w	s	b	c	m	a	o	d
i	a	i	n	c	p	z	v	k
n	r	d	l	k	h	h	e	d
d	b	a	t	l	f	q	r	d

B Match each word from the first box with the correct **preposition** from
the second box.
Write the pairs of words.

rely	to
different	for
similar	with
angry	on
good	from

1 _____

2 _____

3 _____

4 _____

5 _____

Nelson Grammar   © Wendy Wren 1998   Published by Thomas Nelson and Sons Ltd.

A In some of the sentences below, 'a' and 'an' are used incorrectly. Can you put them right?

1 A army of ants built an nest. _____

2 I am buying a house. _____

3 We have to wear an uniform. _____

4 A eel swam in the stream. _____

5 In a hour we can go home. _____

6 May I have an apple? _____

B Complete the table by writing ten words you would use with 'a' and ten words you would use with 'an'.

Words you use with 'a'		Words you use with 'an'	
_____	_____	_____	_____
_____	_____	_____	_____
_____	_____	_____	_____
_____	_____	_____	_____
_____	_____	_____	_____

C Choose two 'a' words and two 'an' words and put them in sentences of your own.

1 a _____

2 a _____

3 an _____

4 an _____

Nelson Grammar © Wendy Wren 1998 Published by Thomas Nelson and Sons Ltd.

name _____   date _____

Use the **past tense** to write about what is happening in the picture.
Underline all the **past tense verbs** you use.

Nelson Grammar © Wendy Wren 1998 Published by Thomas Nelson and Sons Ltd.

A Write *where, were* or *we're* in the gaps to complete these sentences.

1 If .... quick we will see the start of the film.

2 I do not know .... I put the newspaper.

3 The boys had climbed the tree and .... stuck.

4 I am not sure .... the spade is.

5 I knew you .... in a hurry this morning.

B Write *there* or *their* in the gaps to complete these sentences.

1 If we go over .... we'll be able to see more.

2 I like .... new coats.

3 .... are no apples left in the bowl.

4 My grandparents said I could go to .... house for tea.

5 .... is a pear tree in .... garden.

C Use the words below in sentences of your own.

1 where _____

_____

2 were _____

_____

3 we're _____

_____

4 there _____

_____

5 their _____

name _____ date _____

A Underline the **plural** words.

desks	fox	swamp	torches	jugs	boxes
church	floors	wall	inches	lamp	lunches

B Write the **plurals** of these singular words.

1 glass _____ 2 cap _____

3 elephant _____ 4 stitch _____

5 bird _____ 6 tax _____

7 hunch _____ 8 hand _____

9 light _____ 10 marsh _____

11 hammer _____ 12 porch _____

C Write the singular words for these **plurals**.

Singular	Plural
1 _____	foxes
2 _____	rashes
3 _____	atlases
4 _____	gases

Nelson Grammar © Wendy Wren 1998 Published by Thomas Nelson and Sons Ltd.

A In each sentence, underline the **adverb**.
Put a ring around the **verb** it is describing.
Write whether it is a *how*, *when* or *where* adverb.
The first one has been done for you.

1   The crowd (cheered) loudly at the football match.   *how* _____

2   Donisha jumped up when the bell rang.   _____

3   The snake hissed suddenly.   _____

4   You can go early if you have finished.   _____

5   The spider spun busily to make its web.   _____

B Underline the **pairs of adverbs** in these

1   The time went rather quickly.

2   You must draw the map very neatly.

3   I go to that shop most often.

4   He spoke so quietly I could hardly hear him.

5   This is quite firmly stuck together.

C Use the **pairs of adverbs** below in sentences of your own.

1   only slowly _____

_____

2   more frequently _____

_____

3   less often _____

_____

A Complete this table by adding the **past tense** of the verbs.

Verb family name	Past tense
to grow	I _____
to play	you _____
to swim	we _____
to jump	they _____
to write	I _____
to draw	you _____
to give	we _____
to live	they _____
to come	I _____

B Write *present tense* or *past tense* beside each sentence.

1   We sing at school on Tuesdays.   _____

2   The flowers grew in the garden.   _____

3   They are running a race.   _____

4   The baby had rice pudding for tea.   _____

5   They were sorry about the broken window.   _____

C Use a dictionary to find the **past tense** of these verbs.

1   to fight   _____   2   to meet   _____

3   to bind   _____   4   to buy   _____

5   to mean   _____   6   to seek   _____

Nelson
GRAMMAR

BOOK 2
Unit 19
Copymaster

name _____ date _____

A Use each of these **verbs** in a sentence of your own.

1 *are flying* --

----

2 *stopped* --

----

3 *were swimming* --

----

4 *comes* --

B Make each of these into a sentence by adding a **verb** and
any other words you need.
Underline the **verb** in each sentence.

1 The two children ---

----

2 The old house ---

----

3 Everybody ---

----

4 In the jungle --

----

5 Look at ---

Improve Your Writing
Copymaster 1

name _____ date _____

Adjectives describe nouns and make our writing more interesting.
Look at this picture of a dragon.

Write as many interesting **adjectives** as you can to describe the dragon.

------------------ ------------------ ------------------ ------------------

------------------ ------------------ ------------------ ------------------

------------------ ------------------ ------------------ ------------------

Use your **adjectives** to write some sentences to describe the dragon.
Remember to use capital letters and full stops.

Nelson Grammar © Wendy Wren 1998 Published by Thomas Nelson and Sons Ltd.

Improve Your Writing
Copymaster 2

name _____ date _____

In this picture, you can see a cat, a spade, a chair, a dog, a man, a dustbin and a book. We could say that all these things are **in** the garden.

We can make our writing more interesting by using **prepositions** to say **exactly** where things are.

Write sentences, using **prepositions**, to say **exactly** where each of these things is. The first one has been done for you.

dustbin   The dustbin is behind the wall. ....

cat   ....

spade   ....

chair   ....

dog   ....

man   ....

book   ....

Improve Your Writing

Copymaster 3

name _____ date _____

Here is a family – a man, a woman, a boy, a girl and a dog.

If you were writing about this family, calling them 'the man', 'the woman', 'the boy', 'the girl' and 'the dog' would be very boring.

Using **proper nouns** would make your writing more interesting.

Think of an interesting name for each member of the family.

Write about the family, using their names.

Remember that you can use the **pronouns** *he, she, it* or *they*, so you do not have to keep repeating their names.

Improve Your Writing
Copymaster 4

name _____ date _____

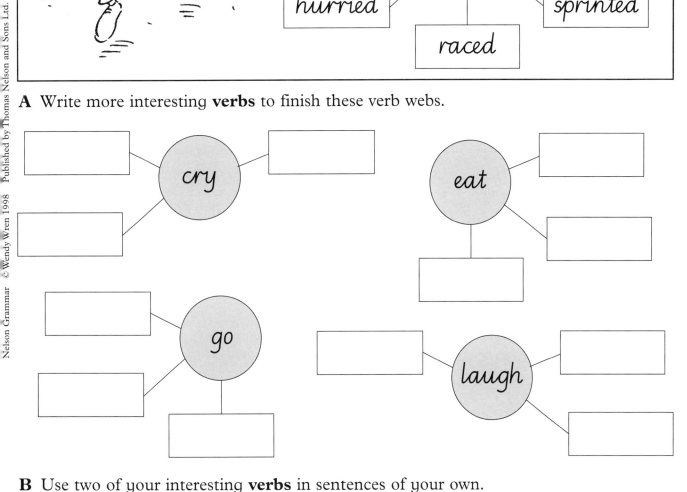

Think carefully about the **verbs** you use.

Todd ran down the road.

We could use more interesting words than 'ran'.

rushed — ran — dashed

hurried — sprinted

raced

A Write more interesting **verbs** to finish these verb webs.

cry

eat

go

laugh

B Use two of your interesting **verbs** in sentences of your own.

Improve Your Writing
Copymaster 5

name _____ date _____

Nelson Grammar © Wendy Wren 1998 Published by Thomas Nelson and Sons Ltd.

We use **conjunctions** to make some sentences longer than others.
Using sentences of different lengths makes writing more interesting.

Too many short sentences can be quite boring to read:

I was hungry. I made a sandwich. I had cheese in my sandwich. There was no jam.

Using conjunctions makes this easier to read and more interesting:

I was hungry <u>so</u> I made a sandwich. I had cheese in my sandwich <u>because</u> there was no jam.

A Join these pairs of sentences with **conjunctions**.

1 I have finished this book. I did not like it.

----

2 Naomi bought some apples. She bought some cakes.

B Write sentences of your own using these **conjunctions**.

1 although ---

----

2 while ---

----

3 until ---

Adverbs make our writing more interesting by telling the reader **how**, **when** or **where** an action takes place.

A Add an **adverb** to each sentence to say **how** the action is being done.

1 The teacher smiled _____ at the boy.

2 The book fell _____ to the floor.

3 The dog barked _____ at the stranger.

B Add an **adverb** to each sentence to say **when** the action is being done.

1 I go swimming _____ .

2 It rained _____ .

3 _____ we walk to school.

C Add an **adverb** to each sentence to say **where** the action is being done.

1 Put the box _____ .

2 I can't find the cat _____ .

3 I saw someone I knew _____ .

D Write about how you travel to school.
Include at least five **adverbs**.

Rewrite the passage below.
Add **adjectives** and **adverbs** to make it more interesting.

Remember, **adjectives** describe nouns and **adverbs** tell us how,
when or where an action takes place.

One night, when the clouds covered the moon and the
stars, there was a noise in the wood. A badger scuttled from
one tree to another and an owl flew on to the branch of a tree.
There was that noise again! There was a light at the edge of
the wood. The night creatures hid in the shadows, waiting to
see what would happen.
